HENDRIX

ARE YOU EXPERIENCED

CW00406592

EASY GUITAR TRANSCRIPTIONS COMPLETE WITH LESSONS

GUITAR EASY
RECORDED VERSIONS

WITH NOTES AND TABLATURE

© Copyright 1989 Experience Hendrix L.L.C. (ASCAP)
Order No.AM91386
ISBN 0-7119-3653-6
All Rights Reserved. International Copyright Secured.

Exclusive distributors for EC and EFTA countries (United Kingdom, Eire, Norway,
Denmark, Sweden, Finland, Belgium, Holland, Luxembourg, France, Germany, Italy,
Spain, Portugal, Greece, Austria and Switzerland) and Australasia:
Music Sales Limited, 8/9 Frith Street, London W1V 5TZ.
Music Sales Pty Limited, 120 Rothschild Avenue, Rosebery, NSW 2018, Australia.

CONTENTS

INTRODUCTION

This publication is presented for the beginning player who is looking for a realistic way to get into the music of Jimi Hendrix. Obviously, it would be quite difficult for anyone who is just starting out with the guitar to play his music. However, we feel that this publication will fill a need for exciting, accurate and challenging music for the beginner.

Presented here are off-the-record chord voicings and licks, along with some nice introductory lessons to go with each song. The more difficult solos are not included, but can be found in a more advanced publication - the Guitar Recorded Versions entitled 'Hendrix: Are You Experienced?' (Order No. AM91387)

Keep Rockin'

The Editorial Staff

PURPLE HAZE

LESSON

The introduction to *Purple Haze* is probably the most famous example in music of the tritone, a very harsh and dissonant two-note relationship of, in this case, E and B♭. The tritone also goes under the aliases augmented fourth (a fourth raised one fret) or diminished fifth (a fifth lowered one fret). Fourths and fifths are common in music and pleasant to hear, but that note in between the fourth and fifth creates a harmony that will grab you by the collar! Use it only when you want to incite maximum disturbance.

One challenging spot in this tune is the measure following the opening tritones where you apply vibrato following a slight bend on the G. There are different ways to produce vibrato, but the way suggested here involves swiveling or rotating back and forth at the wrist as you fret the note. This motion should swing the pinky side of your hand out and in. Your fretting finger (either the index or middle in this case) will want to follow, bending the string back and forth with it. If this is done properly you will notice a leveraging action on the side of your index, which helps to bend the string.

This type of vibrato should be done tastefully. If you overdo it, you will begin to sound like a hawaiian guitar player from the bottom of a lagoon. Just remember that the wavieness of the vibrato is a function of how far your hand flutters.

PURPLE HAZE

Words and Music by JIMI HENDRIX

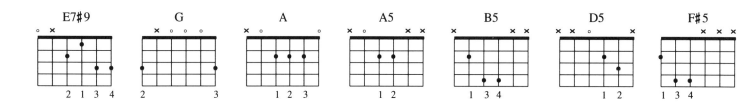

Introduction

Moderate Rock ♩ = 112

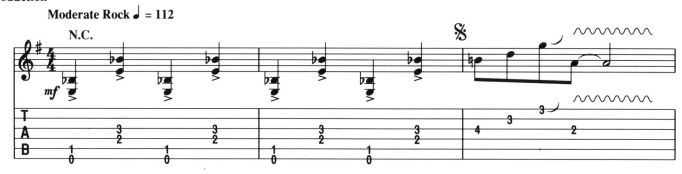

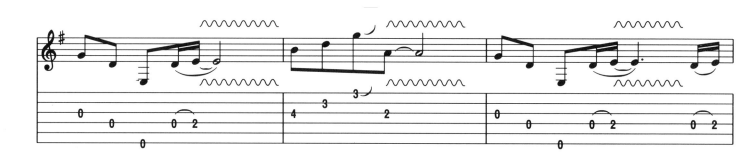

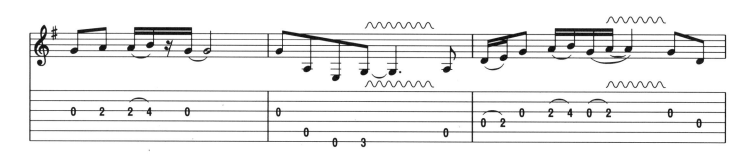

(On D.S. go directly to 3rd verse)

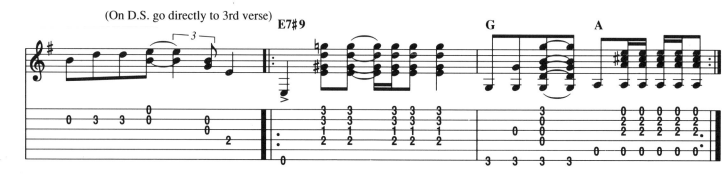

Here is an example of a musical device known as counterpoint, wherein two or more melodies are played simultaneously. The first melody belongs to you the singer and the second melody belongs to you the guitarist.

If you read the guitar part as written, you will probably sense that something isn't quite right. All the eighth note pairs need to swing, that is to say you should apply a triplet feel to each pair of eighths. One way to understand this is to impose syllables on the notes in question. The verbalization will clue you in to the desired rhythm. Here's how the opening riff sounds, if played literally as written:

Here's how it sounds if the eighth notes "swing":

Why don't they just write what they mean? Because notating every swung rhythm is a lot of extra unnecessary work if the musician is simply aware that eighth note pairs are to be swung. So, now you're aware! But watch out, not all eighth notes in this book are swung. Your best reference is the recording itself.

By the way, the tiny grace notes you see tied to some of the notes (like on the second beat of the verse) represent a legato slide. Both notes are fretted with the same finger. Slide the grace note and land on the big note. Make sure your big notes, not the graces, land on the beat.

MANIC DEPRESSION

Words and Music by JIMI HENDRIX

Introduction

Moderate Rock ♩ = 152

Verse

1. Man - ic de - pres - sion ___ is   touch - in' my
2. Wo - man so   wear - y ___   the sweet cause in
   think I'll go   turn my - self off and, uh   go on ___

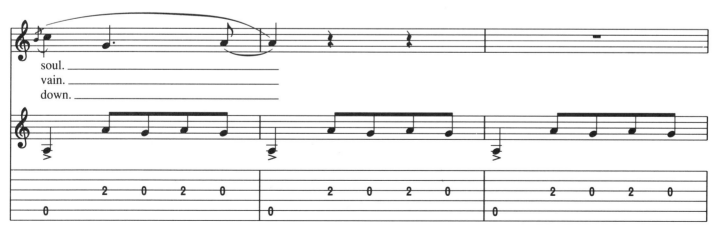

soul. ___
vain. ___
down. ___

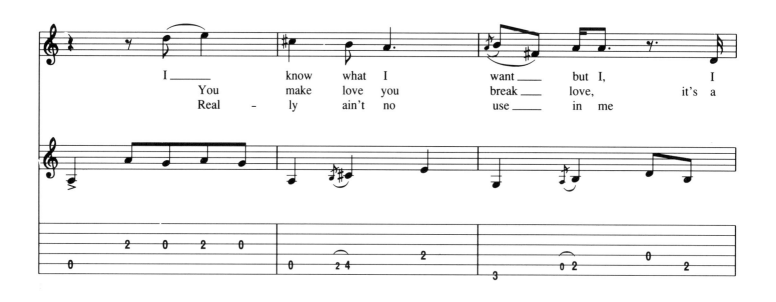

I _____ know what I want _____ but I, I
You know make love you break _____ love, it's a
Real - ly ain't no use _____ in me

just don't _____ know _____ how to, heh!   Go a - bout
all _____ the same, _____ when it's,
hang - in' a - round _____ in, uh,   when it's o -
your _____

get - tin' it.
- ver. _____   Feel - in' sweet
kind - a scene.   Mu - sic sweet
Mu - sic, sweet

To Coda ⊕

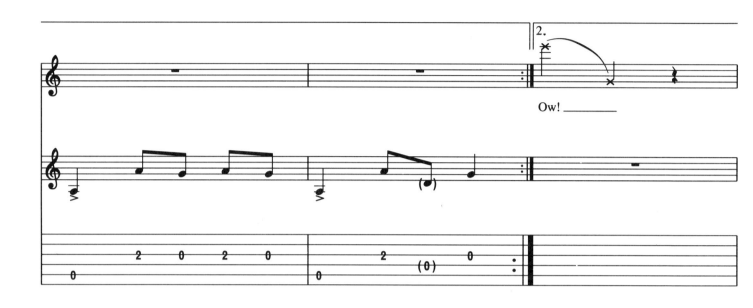

Ow! ____

Guitar Solo

D.S. 𝄋 al Coda ⊕

34

3. Well, I

34

Coda
⊕

Repeat and Fade
(Vocal Ad Lib)

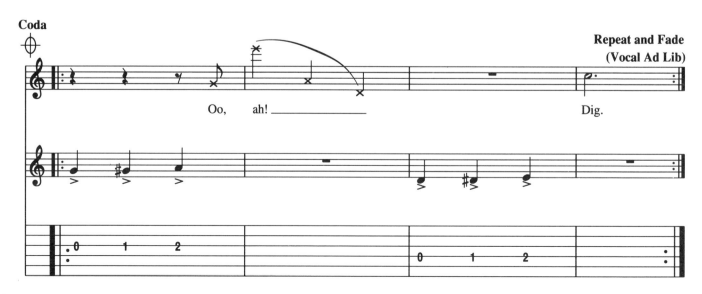

Oo, ah! ____ Dig.

HEY JOE

LESSON

Hendrix plays the notes within these chords very selectively, preferring two and three note strums to full five- or six-string folk strums. So don't let the lyrics about hangings and fleeing the law to Mexico persuade you to strum full chords like a cowpoke! Part of the Hendrix style here also comes from very light, downward strums, playing a series of sixteenth note strums with all down strokes instead of alternating the strums up and down.

Hendrix was one of the first guitarists to make viable the "power trio" performing format, wherein the guitar takes on both the rhythm and lead roles. It takes extraordinary versatility to succeed in this setting. You can get some clues as to how Hendrix achieved this by studying the introduction, as well as last two bars of the piece, both of which expand upon the first position E chord. These excerpts will give you ideas for making your rhythm guitar playing a vital and interesting part of the overall musical texture.

HEY JOE

Words and Music by BILLY ROBERTS

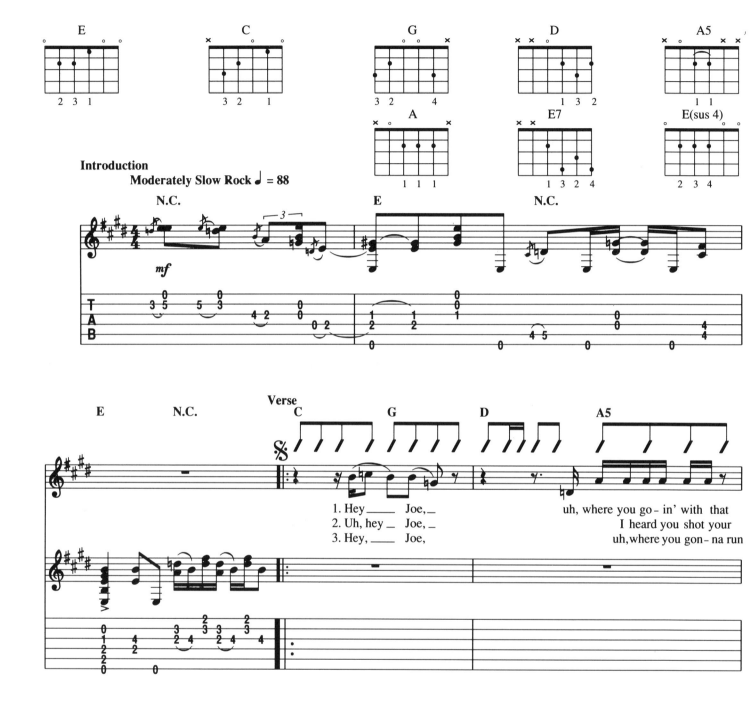

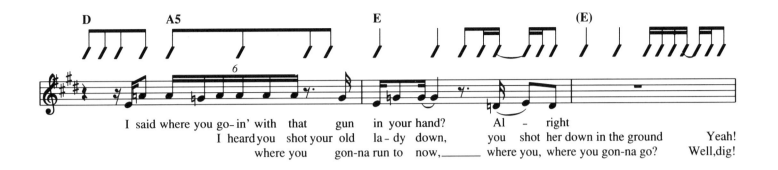

I said where you go-in' with that gun in your hand? Al - right
I heard you shot your old la - dy down, you shot her down in the ground Yeah!
where you gon-na run to now,_____ where you, where you gon-na go? Well, dig!

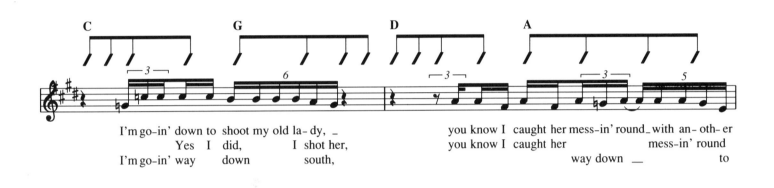

I'm go-in' down to shoot my old la-dy, _ you know I caught her mess-in' round_ with an-oth-er
Yes I did, I shot her, you know I caught her mess-in' round
I'm go-in' way down south, way down _ to

man. Yeah!
mess-in' round town. Al – right!
Mex - i - co way!

I'm go-in' down to shoot my old la-dy,
Uh, yes I did, I shot her,
I'm go-in' way down south,

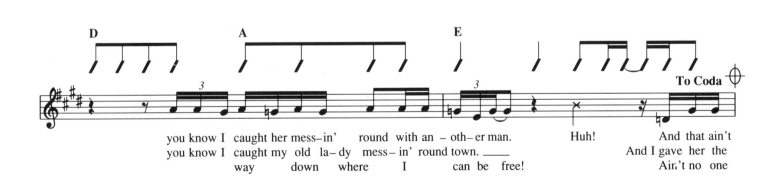

you know I caught her mess-in' round with an-oth-er man. Huh! And that ain't
you know I caught my old la-dy mess-in' round town. ____ And I gave her the
way down where I can be free! Ain't no one

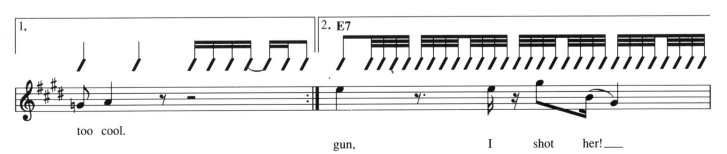

too cool.

gun, I shot her!___

__ gon-na find me, babe!   Ain't no hang-man gon-na,   he ain't gon-na put a rope a-round

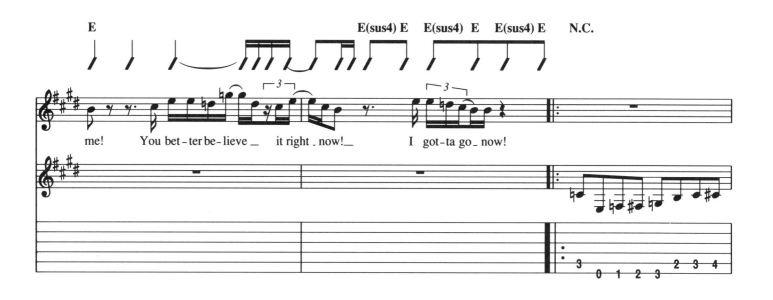

me!   You bet-ter be-lieve __ it right _ now!__   I got-ta go_ now!

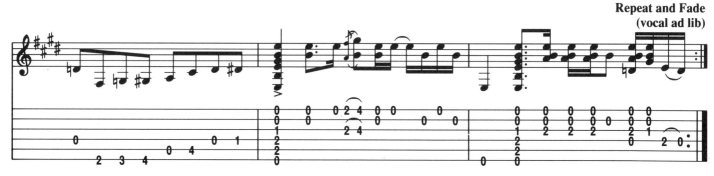

LOVE OR CONFUSION

LESSON

There are some chords in this piece that may require explaining, like the F(sus2)/G and the F/G. Let's find out what this mysterious nomenclature means, beginning with the simpler of the two, F/G. Is this chord an F, or a G, or a just case of chordal schizophrenia?

None of the above. F/G, which can be pronounced "F over G," is nothing more than an F chord on top of a low G note. Here is a formula for figuring it out on your own. First, find the lowest G note available on your guitar (if you have to think too hard on this one you've got some boning up to do…) Are you thinking 3rd fret of the 6th string? Now, find an F chord within reach on any combination of the remaining strings. Remember that whatever finger you assigned to that G note can be changed in favor of another finger that makes the chord playable.

So, slash chords like this represent a chord over a specific lower note. But what about F(sus2)/G? As the name implies, this is a slight variation on our original F/G, involving the addition to the F chord of a sus 2 (suspended 2nd). What's a 2nd in F? Answer: G. Now add a G note to the F chord, and don't be afraid of dropping another note in the chord to achieve this. Check the F(sus2)/G provided in the music against your concoction.

As you can see, chord names are simply recipes identifying the ingredients of the chord in question. If you know a few basic rules and the notes on your guitar, you can build any chord you see from scratch, as well as name the ones you invent yourself.

The chord work in *Love or Confusion* also contains some good examples of syncopation, an important rhythmic device that is found in all types of music. Syncopation can be defined as a pattern that displaces the normal rhythmic stress by emphasizing beats, or subdivisions of beats, that would normally be unstressed.

The hierarchy of rhythmic importance in a 4/4 measure gives the 1st and 3rd beats the most emphasis:

"strong" "weak" "strong" "weak"

If the measure is divided into eighth notes, the same strong-weak pattern emerges:

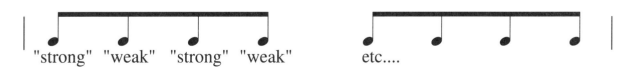

"strong" "weak" "strong" "weak"   etc….

LOVE OR CONFUSION

Words and Music by JIMI HENDRIX

© Copyright 1967 by Experience Hendrix L.L.C. (ASCAP)
P.O. Box 88376 Seattle, Washington 98138 USA
All Rights Reserved. International Copyright Secured

MAY THIS BE LOVE

LESSON

The introduction loosely represents the sound of a bottleneck slide descending over the open strings. The intention is to produce a general waterfall effect, as opposed to any specific melody or note sequence. Play the notes as written, and bring out the cascading effect with your phrasing.

Speaking of water, Jimi's ultra-fluid chording style here, as it is in other tunes on this album, is achieved with the help of major pentatonic scales related to the chords being played. You can float, for instance, from an E to F♭m7(add4)/E to A(add2) in the verse with E major pentatonic, a scale that relates to all those chords nicely. The five notes in E major pentatonic are E-F♯-G♯-B-C♯ (which are the 1st, 2nd, 3rd, 5th and 6th of E major.) Identify these notes in the first position on the lower sounding strings and you will discover a pattern to mix freely into the three chords. (If you want to think technically, each chord has its own most appropriate major or minor pentatonic scale. However, E major pentatonic relates closely enough to all three chords that we can consider it the pattern to get through the chord sequence with.)

To integrate chords with this scale, play the chords as you would normally and slip in your scale embellishments with whatever fingers are available.

There are other major pentatonics to be discovered on the bridge (more water allusions). Construct these yourself over the D, A and B chords. Simply identify the 1st, 2nd, 3rd, 5th and 6th in each of the D, A, and B major scales and you can do some chord floating of your own.

P.S. Don't let your ear be confused by another common chordal adornment that Hendrix uses, the suspended 4th. That would be an A (2nd fret, 3rd string) in the E major chord.

MAY THIS BE LOVE

Words and Music by JIMI HENDRIX

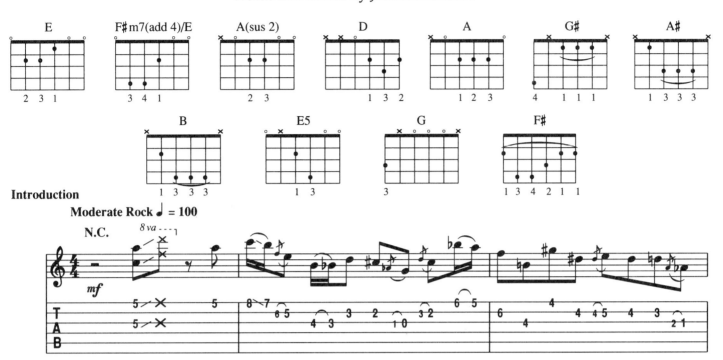

Introduction

Moderate Rock ♩ = 100

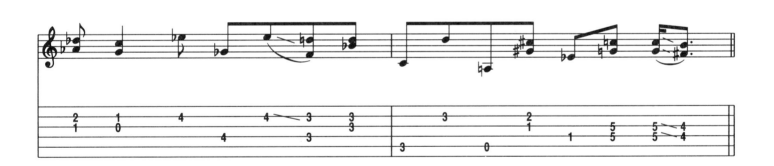

Verse

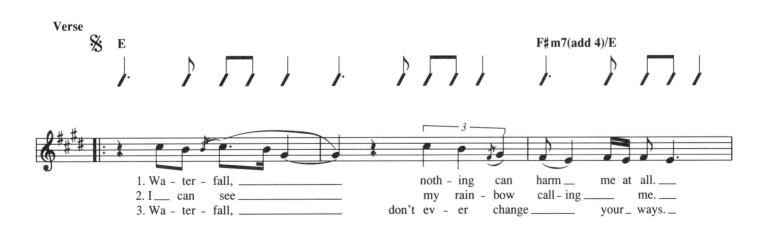

1. Wa - ter - fall, _____ noth - ing can harm _ me at all. _
2. I _ can see _____ my rain - bow call - ing _____ me. _
3. Wa - ter - fall, _____ don't ev - er change _____ your _ ways. _

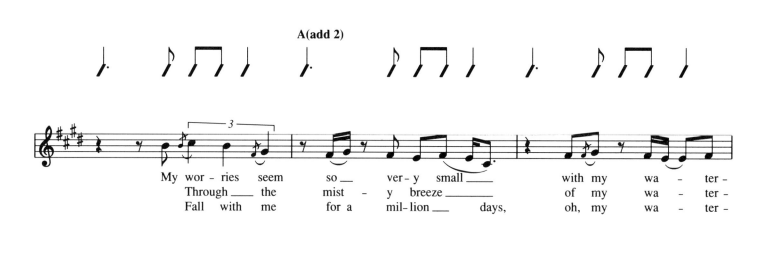

My wor - ries seem so __ ver - y small __ with my wa - ter-
Through __ the mist - y breeze __ of my wa - ter-
Fall with me for a mil - lion __ days, oh, my wa - ter-

To Coda ⊕

Bridge D

- fall.
- fall.
- fall.

Some peo - ple say

day - dream - in's for all the, huh! la - zy mind - ed fools __ with noth - in' else_

_ to __ do. _ So let them laugh, laugh _ at _ me.

So just as long ___ as I have you ___ to see me through. I have ___ noth-ing to

D.S. 𝄋 al Coda ⨁

lose. 'long ___ as I ___ have you.

Coda

⨁ **Guitar Solo**

Repeat and Fade

I DON'T LIVE TODAY

LESSON

The solo in this song utilizes two scales that are very similar: B mixolydian and B dorian. Let's lay them out on your top 3 strings (E, B and G) and experiment with Hendrix's sitar-like approach to the solo.

There are different ways to think of these scales, but let's relate them to a major, do-re-mi type scale, which in B is:

1	2	3	4	5	6	7	8
B	C♯	D♯	E	F♯	G♯	A♯	B

The B mixolydian scale, commonly played over dominant 7th chords, is created by simply lowering the 7th scale degree in the major scale by one fret:

1	2	3	4	5	6	♭7	8
B	C♯	D♯	E	F♯	G♯	A	B

Learn these notes on your top two or three strings and experiment with them, sliding up and down through the scale on each string.

Now for the B dorian scale, which is associated with minor chords and involves a lowering of the 3rd and the 7th scale degree in the major scale:

1	2	♭3	4	5	6	♭7	8
B	C♯	D	E	F♯	G♯	A	B

You don't have to learn a whole new scale to apply this to your axe. Simply remember your B mixolydian and alter the 3rd, lowering all your D♯s one fret to D. Now you can improvise, slipping back and forth as you wish between the regular and lowered third. Both 3rds sound fine because neither third is being emphasized by any other instrument. So it's up to the soloist to define the thirdness of the music at any given point.

And how does the neophyte guitarist attain true sitarness with these scales? Only your guru can answer that completely, but you can achieve an approximation, as does Hendrix, by sliding up and down single strings with lots of glisses, hammer-ons and pull-offs. Sitting in the lotus postion might help too.

I DON'T LIVE TODAY

Words and Music by JIMI HENDRIX

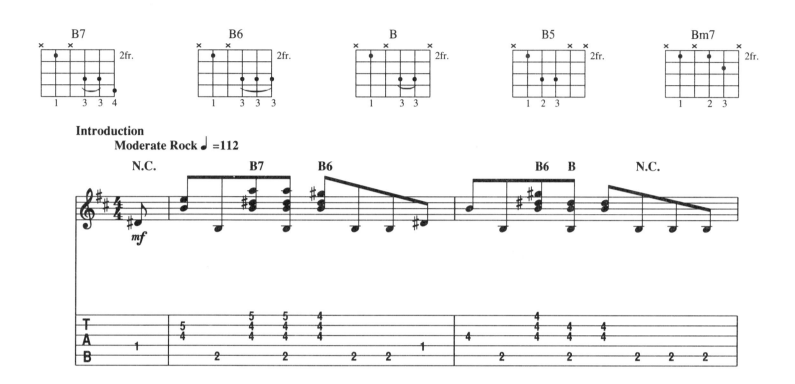

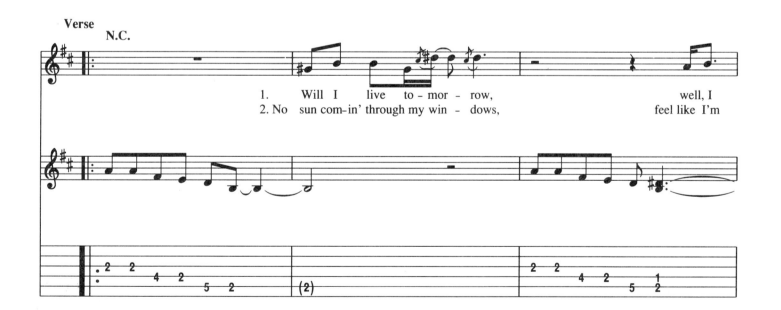

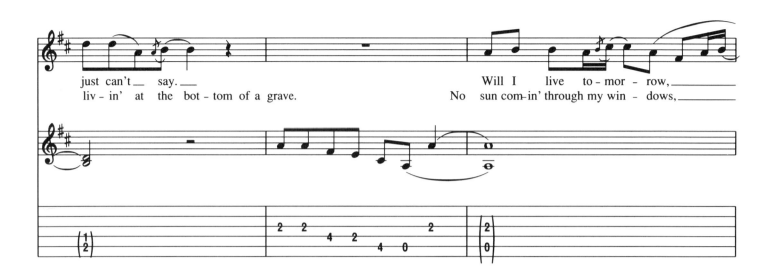

just can't__ say.__
liv-in' at the bot-tom of a grave.
Will I live to-mor-row,_____
No sun com-in' through my win-dows,_____

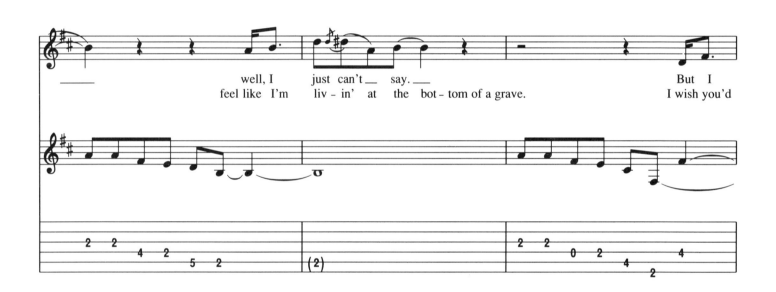

_____ well, I just can't__ say.__
feel like I'm liv-in' at the bot-tom of a grave.
But I
I wish you'd

2nd verse only **B5**

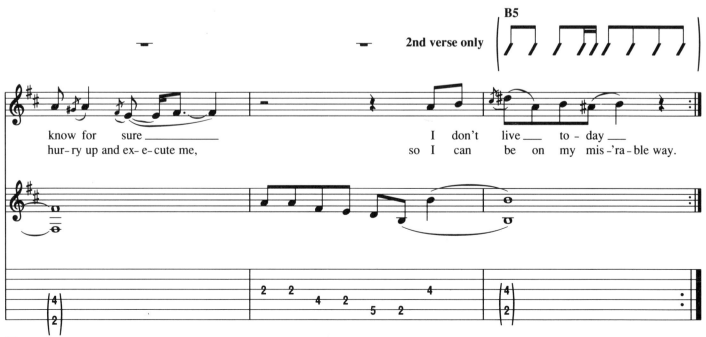

know for sure _____
hur-ry up and ex-e-cute me,
I don't live__ to-day__
so I can be on my mis-'ra-ble way.

Chorus
Bm7

Well, I don't ___ live ___ to - day, ___ may - be to-mor - row

(Bm7)

I just can't ___ say, ___ but, uh, I don't ___ live ___ to - day. ___

1.

Guitar Solo

16

It's such a shame to waste your time a - way like this. ___

2.   N.C.
                                           A(5th fret)   F♯(2nd fret)   B♭(6th fret)   B(7th fret)

spend ___ the time...   a - way like this...   ex - ist - ing...

N.C.   Repeat and Fade

THE WIND CRIES MARY

LESSON

It is rare to find examples of refined understatement in rock, but here it is! One aspect of musical artistry is the ability to convey a wide range of emotions and moods. In a nutshell, your hard-driving ear blaster with the screaming solo will have more impact if it is coupled with a ballad like this, which features lyrical and unpretentious chording and soloing.

The introduction is a good study of chord inversion and content, wherein the notes of a given chord are arranged in differing order to achieve variety and chordal motion. The first measure presents an E♭5 chord. The number 5 signifies that the third of the chord, G, is omitted, leaving the notes E♭ and the fifth, B♭. Note also that the lowest note in this "voicing" is not the root E♭, but the fifth B♭. There are all sorts of ways to pile these two notes on top of each other, if you consider that more than one of each note can be included.

The second measure begins with E♭/G, which is yet another version of E♭, this time with its third, G, on the bottom. In this chord, all three notes of E♭ are included: E♭, G and B♭. We call it an "inversion" because these three notes have been tumbled to establish another note in the bass. (Don't be confused by the grace note, which leads us from the 2nd to the 3rd.) Again, there are countless ways to arrange combinations of these notes across the fingerboard.

The remaining two chords in these first measures are simply the E♭s moved up fret by fret to become E♮ and F♯.

You will notice from the recording that Hendrix definitely knew his various inversions. Once you can play this tune with the chords provided, your mission, using your ears and brains, is to seek out the myriad of inversions that Hendrix uses.

THE WIND CRIES MARY

Words and Music by JIMI HENDRIX

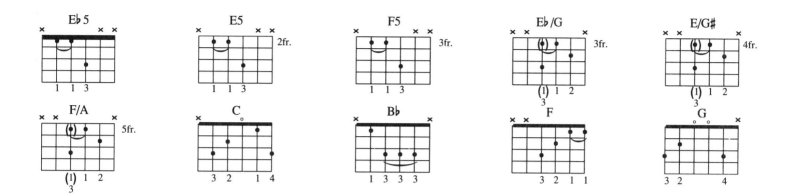

Introduction

Verse

1. Af – ter all the jacks ___ are in their box – es, and the clowns have all gone to
2. A broom is drear – i – ly sweep – ing ___ up the bro – ken piec – es of yes – ter – day's
3. The traf – fic lights, they turn uh, blue to – mor – row, and Shine their emp – ti – ness down on my
4. Uh, will the wind ev – er re – mem – ber the names it has blown in the

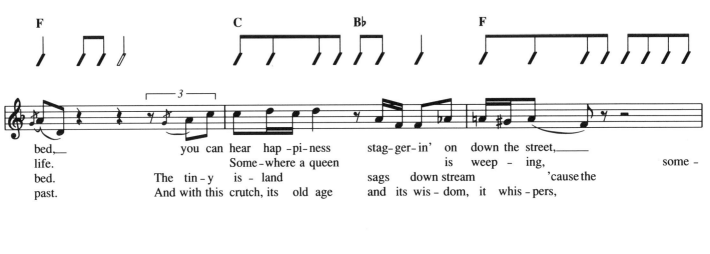

bed,_____ you can hear hap-pi-ness stag-ger-in' on down the street,_____
life._____ Some-where a queen is weep-ing, some-
bed._____ The tin-y is-land sags down stream 'cause the
past._____ And with this crutch, its old age and its wis-dom, it whis-pers,

foot-prints dressed in red. ____ And the wind _____ whis-pers
where ___ a king has no wife. And the wind, _____ it cries
life that lived is, is dead. And the wind _____ screams
"No, this will be the last." And the wind _____ cries

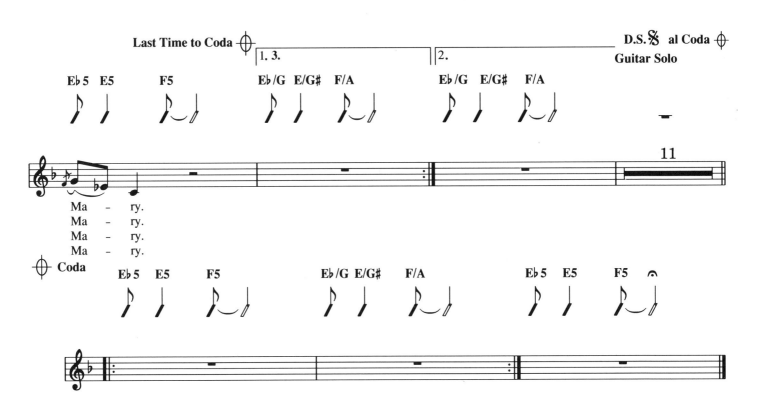

Last Time to Coda ⊕

D.S. 𝄋 **al Coda** ⊕

Guitar Solo

Ma - ry.
Ma - ry.
Ma - ry.
Ma - ry.

⊕ **Coda**

FIRE

LESSON

Here is eveything you need to get started playing octaves on the guitar. What's an octave? It's the distance between any note and the nearest other note of the same letter name. Playing a line in octaves beefs it up considerably as you can hear in the introduction. One thing you will notice early on is that there are different ways to finger octaves on the fingerboard, depending on which strings you play them on. Remember that the guitar is tuned differently between the 2nd and 3rd strings than it is between all other adjacent pairs. Since octaves always straddle a string, any octave that straddles the 2nd or 3rd string will require a different fingering. The best way to understand this rule is to discover it yourself, in the introduction. You will find that some octave fingerings cover a distance of three frets while others cover a distance of four frets.

This tune also contains two "add 9" chords, something you may not be familiar with. Remember that an octave is an interval of an eighth? Add another whole step, which is like two frets on the guitar, and you have a ninth. Identify the note for the chord in question and add it in somewhere high in the voicing. For a C chord, then, "add 9" means add a D. For a D chord it means add an E. Now check the two add 9s in this tune and see how it works.

FIRE

Words and Music by JIMI HENDRIX

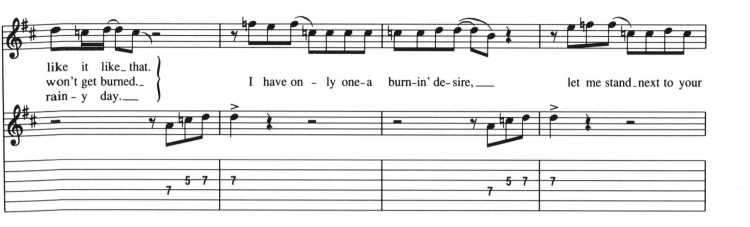

like it like that.
won't get burned.
rain - y day.

I have on - ly one-a burn-in' de-sire, ____

let me stand next to your

Chorus

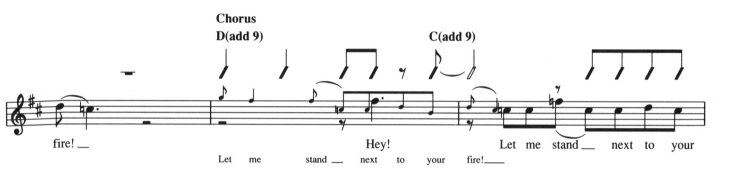

D(add 9)   C(add 9)

fire! ____

Let me   stand ____ next to your fire! ____

Hey!   Let me stand ____ next to your

D(add 9)   C(add 9)   D(add 9)   C(add 9)

fire!

Let me   stand ____ next to your   fire! ____

Whoa, __ let me stand ____ ba - by!

Let me   stand ____ next to your

To Coda ⊕   ‖1.

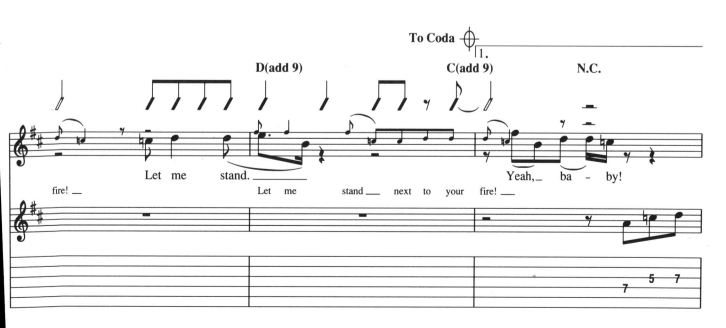

D(add 9)   C(add 9)   N.C.

Let me   stand. ____   Yeah, __ ba - by!

fire! ____   Let me   stand ____ next to your fire! ____

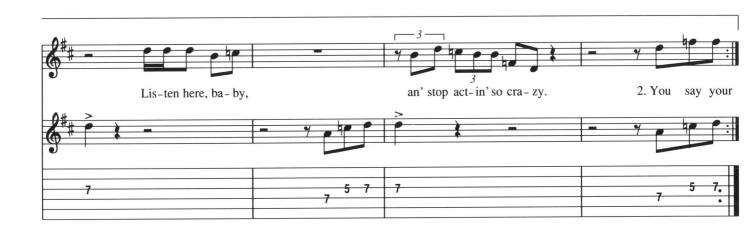

Lis-ten here, ba - by, an' stop act-in' so cra - zy. 2. You say your

Bridge
D5 **C5**

Ow! Ah, __ move o - ver, __ Ro-ver, __ and let Jim- i take
fire! ____

A

o – ver! Yeah, you know what I'm talk - in' a - bout!

C5 **Guitar Solo** **Repeat 4 times then**
E5 **B5** **D.C. 𝄋 al Coda** ⊕

Yeah! __ Get on with it ba - by!

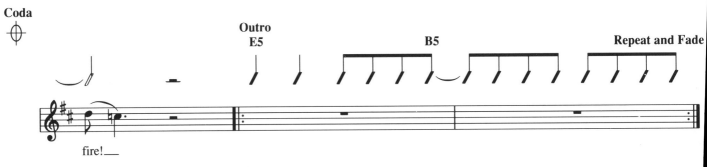

Coda
⊕ **Outro**
E5 **B5** **Repeat and Fade**

fire! __

THIRD STONE FROM THE SUN

LESSON

There are four distinct sections to this composition, each with its own challenges.

The introduction is very much like classical guitar music in its mixture of soloistic techniques. Most challenging is the melodic meandering around on the open E and B strings. Make sure your fingers on the 2nd and 3rd strings don't get in the way of the ringing, droning open strings.

The theme is your second lesson in octaves. Apply what you learned in *Fire*.

The extended free-form-whammy-bar-feedback solo at the end is an expressive form that transcends the written note. This is a style of musical abstraction wherein effects and timbres are treated as emotive shapes – a sound sculpture of sorts. Can you develop a voice of your own in this genre? Bolt your furniture to the floor, turn the lights down and your amp up, and see what happens…

THIRD STONE FROM THE SUN

Words and Music by JIMI HENDRIX

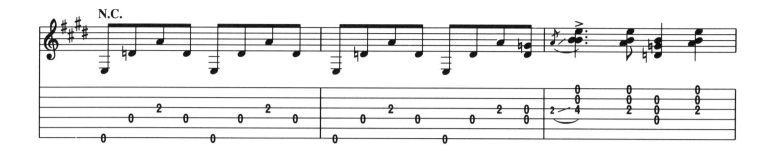
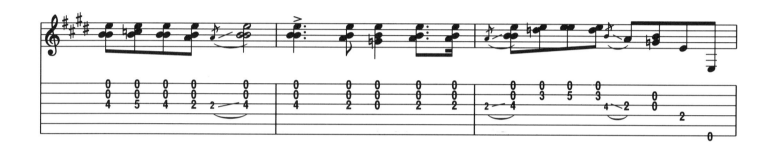

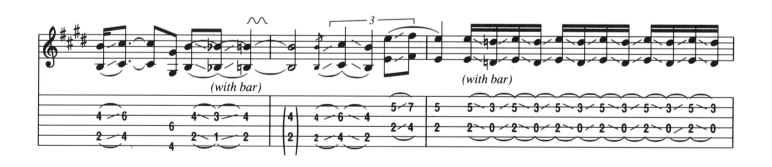

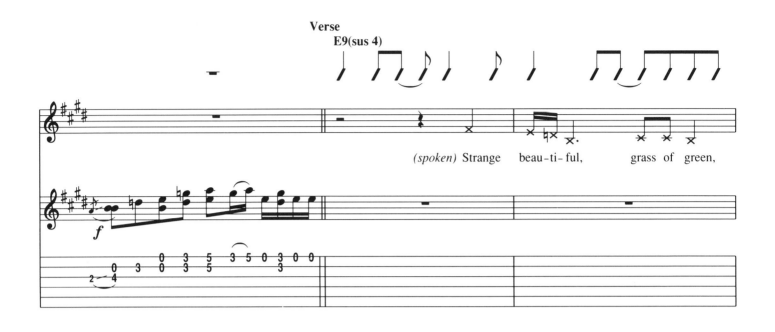

(spoken) Strange beau-ti-ful, grass of green,

with your ma-jes-tic_ sil-ver seas. Your mys-ter-i-ous moun-tains I wish to see clos-er.

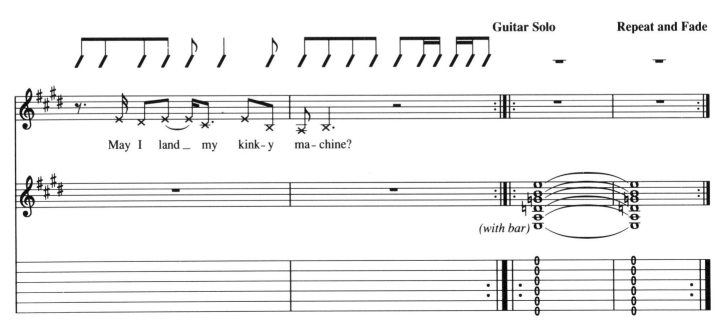

May I land_ my kink-y ma-chine?

(with bar)

FOXY LADY

LESSON

How exactly would you go about strumming the chords in this tune? Many beginning rockers instinctively strum all chords in a downward motion, slashing from the sixth string toward the first. This instinct is correct, since the rock sound is based on the repeated pounding effect this approach produces. But a few artfully placed upstrokes will give your rhythm part some personality and prevent it from sounding like the Jackhammer That Wouldn't Die!

A brief look at the rhythm patterns for *Foxy Lady* reveals that the eighth note strum is the most common rhythm, with a dotted eighth and sixteenth note sprinkled here and there. Let's set up a pattern of eighth note down strums on the chord of your choice as a "template" or base from which we will add variations.

Let's call these the "strong beats" (sounds like a good name for a group!). In order to maintain a down strum on every eighth you have to come back up to get ready for the next strum. Those up motions are available for strumming duty too. If you also strum on each up motion you will have subivided your eighths into sixteenths:

Be aware of which of these sixteenths are the original strong beats. Those are the ones you are still strumming down on. We've simply added a weak beat, or up-strum in between each strong beat. Now we can mix up the rhythm as you will find it in, say, the first measure of the verse:

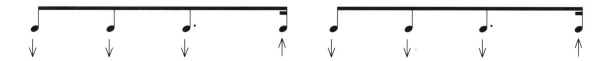

We are still strumming down on the strong beats and up on the weak beats. If this makes sense, you are ready to apply the up-down "template" to all of the rhythms in this tune.

Almost every song has its own pattern of alternating strong and weak beats, and a strumming motion that is approriate to it. And though you don't want this general rule to straitjacket you, it will prevent you from sounding like The Jackhammer That Wouldn't Die!

If you look at the slash notation above the verse, you'll notice that the patterns for the first eight measures are decidedly un-syncopated. These patterns feature strong beats only (such as the whole note strums in the 1st, 3rd and 5th measures of the verse), or if eighth notes are used, all of the "strong" (down), and "weak" (up) beats are played, which has the effect of stressing the downbeats. This straight eighth note pattern is illustrated in the 2nd, 4th, 6th and 8th measures of the verse.

Finally, in the 9th measure we get a break from all of this "normalness." Thus:

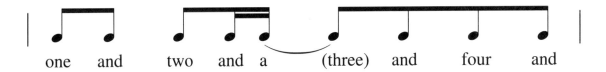

one   and   two   and a   (three) and   four   and

The "3" of the measure is unplayed, shifting the emphasis to the "a" of the second beat. Voila, syncopation!

Notice that the syncopation of the rhythm guitar part is introduced at a point when the bass and drum parts are increasing in complexity and overall excitement. Syncopation achieves a comparable intensifying effect on the rhythm guitar part, without having to resort to getting louder or faster. Look for other examples of this device in Hendrix's music, and check out the lesson to *Foxy Lady* for more discussion of Jimi's rhythm work.

FOXY LADY

Words and Music by JIMI HENDRIX

I won't   do you no harm,___ no. ___   You got-ta be all   mine,_
I'm tired of wast-in' all my   pre-cious time.

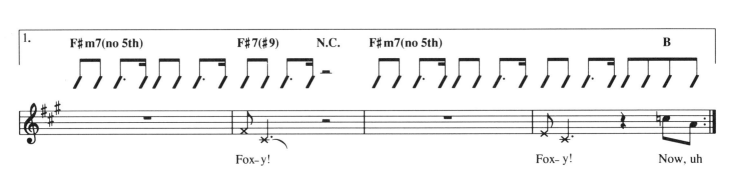

_____ all __ mine. __   Oo!   Fox-y   La-dy!   Yeah!

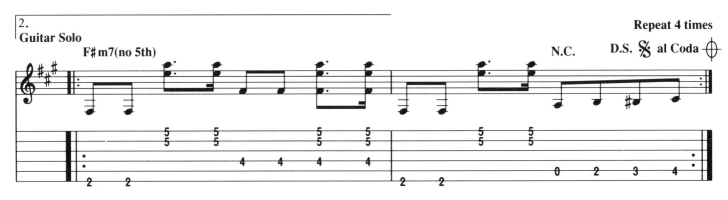

Fox-y!   Fox-y!   Now, uh

Ow!   Fox-y La-dy,_ yeah, yeah,___   You look so   good! __   Fox-y!

ARE YOU EXPERIENCED?

LESSON

Play the muted strings in the introduction by placing your fretting fingers lightly on the strings, touching but not actually depressing them to the fingerboard. (You won't achieve the same sound you hear on the recording without tape processing.) You don't want to hear any pitch at all here, just a sound akin to a snare drum. Strumming muted strings provides a percussive, non-pitched sound that is very exposed rhythmically. You are dealing with pure rhythm here, nothing else.

The most common problem guitarists have with rhythm, on muted strings as well as chords and even solos, is a laziness in their attack that produces a garbled and imprecise sound. Rhythmatists use the word "attack" to refer to the moment sound is initiated on an instrument, and this word describes very well an event that needs to occur with a feeling of immediacy and split-second timing. If your energy level is low your attacks won't succeed; the battle will be won by the forces of mediocrity!

One way to visualize the kind of strumming motion that will sharpen up your attacks is to think of how you would shake a thermometer. The wrist and hand must be completely relaxed so that you can initiate whip-like motions from a loose position, over and over. By relaxing, you allow your arm and hand to move at will, speeding up your response time. Above all, avoid the kind of strumming and picking motion that looks like your hand and arm are sludging through a vat of syrup. If you look lazy and sludgy, you'll sound that way too.

Every single member of any band is a part of the rhythm section, since everyone's sound either contributes to or detracts from the total rhythmic effect of the music. So watch and hear the kind of energy and vitality that all good musicians inject into their parts, and develop the art of the lightning attack!

ARE YOU EXPERIENCED?

Words and Music by JIMI HENDRIX

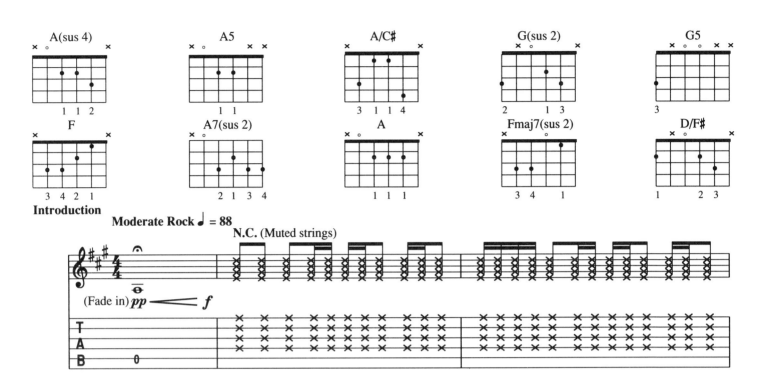

Introduction

Moderate Rock ♩ = 88

N.C. (Muted strings)

(Fade in) *pp* ——— *f*

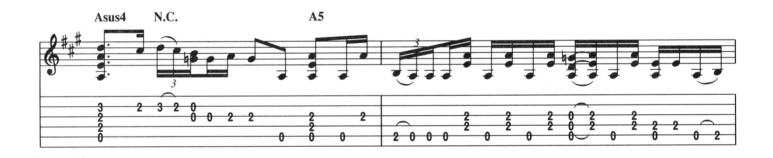

Asus4 N.C. A5

Verses

A/C# Gsus2 A5

1. If you can just   get   your __ mind to-geth-er   uh, then come on a-cross __ to __
2. I know,__ I   know you'll prob-'ly scream and cry   that your lit - tle world won't let you
3. Trum-pets and vi-o-lins   I   can, uh,   hear in the dis-tance,   I think they're call-in' our

A/C♯   Gsus2

___ me.___   We'l hold hands _____ and then we'll   watch _ the sun rise, _____ (uh,)
___ go.___   But who in your meas-ly lit-tle world,   uh, are you try-in' to prove that
___ name.___   May-be now___ you can't hear them,   but you will, _ ha, ha, if you

A5   **Chorus**
                   N.C. (Muted strings)

    from the bot-tom of the sea.
you're made out of gold, _____ and, uh, can't be sold.   But, first,_   are you_ ex -
just take hold of my hand.

G5   F

-per-i-enced?___   Uh, have you ev-er been ex - per - i - enced?_ Uh!   Well,___

                                    Guitar Solo
A5   A7sus2

I _ have. _____

Oh,_____ but are you ex - per - i - enced?_____ Have you ev - er been _ ex - per-

- i - enced? ___ Not nec - es - sar - i – ly stoned, _____ but...

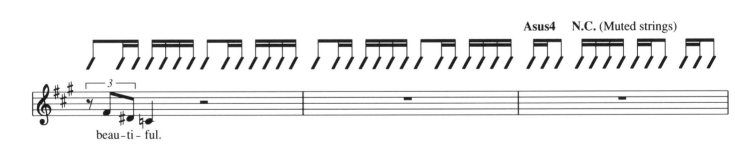

beau - ti - ful.

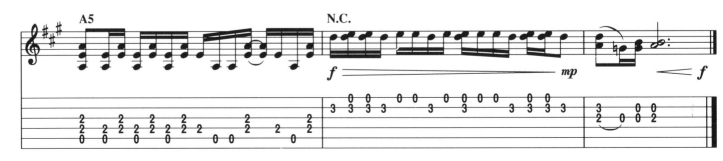

NOTATION LEGEND

Printed in Great Britain by Redwood Books, Trowbridge, Wiltshire   3/97(27263)